This book belongs to

First published in the United Kingdom in 1428[AH] (2007[CE]) by
Learning Roots Ltd.
Unit 6, TGEC, Town Hall Approach Road
London
N15 4RX
www.learningroots.com

Second edition published in 1432[AH] (2011[CE]).
Reprinted in 1433[AH] (2012[CE]).

Authored by Zaheer Khatri.
Illustrations, typsetting and layout by the Learning Roots Education Design Service.

Acknowledgements
The publisher thanks Allah, Lord of the Worlds, for making this publication possible.

British Library Cataloguing in Publication Data
A CIP catalogue record for this book is available from the British Library

Printed and bound in China.

ISBN: 978-1-905516-18-6

the story of Ibrahim عليه السلام

﴿ لَقَدْ كَانَ فِى قَصَصِهِمْ عِبْرَةٌ لِّأُولِى ٱلْأَلْبَٰبِ مَا كَانَ حَدِيثًا يُفْتَرَىٰ وَلَٰكِن تَصْدِيقَ ٱلَّذِى
بَيْنَ يَدَيْهِ وَتَفْصِيلَ كُلِّ شَىْءٍ وَهُدًى وَرَحْمَةً لِّقَوْمٍ يُؤْمِنُونَ ﴾

There is instruction in their stories for people of
intelligence. This is not a narration which has been
invented but confirmation of all that came before, a
clarification of everything, and a guidance and a mercy
for people who have iman.

(The Noble Quran, Surah Yusuf: 111)

contents

You are on a journey.

You will learn about the lives of some of the best men that ever lived.

These were men sent by Allah.

You will learn why they were sent,

who they were sent to,

and what lessons we can learn from their lives.

They are the Prophets.

The first of them is Adam ﷺ

and the last of them is Muhammad ﷺ.

setting off

As with any journey, you will need to know where you are going; having a map of your route certainly helps! On the following pages you will see a map of the Prophets mentioned in the Noble Quran. Follow the path on the map carefully and look out for the names you have heard before.

From amongst all of these Prophets of Allah, five are mentioned in the Quran (in Surah Al-Ahzaab, Ash-Shura & Al-Ahqaaf) as العزم أولوا or Prophets of great determination. They are Nuh عليه السلام, Ibrahim عليه السلام, Musa عليه السلام, Eesa عليه السلام and Muhammad ﷺ. The life of Muhammad ﷺ is a whole subject in and of itself. In this series, we'll take a closer look at the other four Prophets mentioned, as well as the Prophet Adam عليه السلام; the first Prophet of Allah. Take a look at the map on the next page...

Eesa العليه السلام

Ibrahim العليه السلام

Musa العليه السلام

11

As you may have guessed from the title of this book, you'll be learning about the story of Ibrahim ﷺ. You can discover more about the other Prophets in the rest of this series.

As you travel, you will need to acquaint yourself with some essential information. Without it, you will be lost, and may not reach your final destination. Read up on the following symbols to find out what to expect along your way.

*Before you begin any journey, you need to know where you are going and why you are going there. With all the stories in this book, your aim is broken into three parts. You **must** be able to read the story yourself, summarize the main events and place them in the correct order. You **should** be able to understand the finer details of what occurred in the story. Finally, you **could** be able to understand the reasoning behind some of the story events. You will be able to test whether you have achieved your targets at the end of each section by attempting to overcome the obstacles in your way.*

One of the other things you need to do before any journey is to prepare! **Pack Your Bags** *involves reminding yourself about the meanings of some essential key words that occur in the story.*

Once you have set off on your journey, you'll need to think actively about what you are learning. **Reflections** occur in the middle of stories and get you to ponder a little deeper into the events.

Once the reading is over, you'll take a well earned rest at the **Rest Point**. You'll do some light word-work to ensure you understand the language used in the story.

Now begins your chance to prove what you have learnt. You have to cross three different obstacles, each getting harder as you go along. By completing each of these you will ensure you have covered the aims of your journey. First you have to **Jump the Fence** by proving you know enough about the events of the story.

The next task is a little harder. **Cross the River** is all about checking whether you picked up the smaller details of what actually happened in the story.

The final and hardest task is called **Climb the Mountain.** Here you have to show an understanding of why things happened the way they did in the story.

*After completing each section, be sure to have your answers marked in **The Farewell Mark** chapter at the end of this book. Well that's all you need to know before you start! It's time to begin your journey. Bismillah! Here's a little introduction for you...*

Some time went by, but Shaytaan did not rest. People fell for his tricks again. They carved shapes from stones and prayed to them. It seems as thought they never learned. Did they really want to be taught the lesson again?

Before setting off, get familiar with some of the words you will come across in the story. Read the words below and try to make sure you know what they mean before you start. We'll do some work on these and other words at the end of the story.

PROUD

BLAZING

MIRACLE

Allah sent the Prophet Ibrahim *'Alay-his-salaam*. Even as a young child, Ibrahim was very wise.

"Why do you pray to something that cannot see or hear?" he asked his father. "Stones cannot harm you or bring you any good."

But his father didn't want to hear. "If you don't stop I will stone you," he said. "So leave me alone!"

Ibrahim did not give up so easily. He waited until all the town people were away. He picked up his axe. Ibrahim had an idea in mind.

He went up to the stones and smashed them into little bits. He placed his axe on the biggest stone and left it standing. It was all part of his plan.

19

Why do you think Ibrahim عليه السلام left the axe on the largest idol? Why do you think he did not break it like the rest? Write your thoughts in space below and then read on to see if you were right.

The people could not believe their eyes when they returned. "Who has done this to our gods?" they asked in anger.

"The big one did it," said Ibrahim. "So ask them if they are able to speak."

But they were just stones. Stones cannot talk.

"You know that they do not speak," said the people with shame. Ibrahim's plan was working.

"So why do you pray to them instead of Allah?" asked Ibrahim. "Don't you have any sense?"

The people did not know what to say. Ibrahim showed them the truth in such a clever way. But they were too proud and turned away.

"Let's throw him into a blazing fire!" they said with rage.

They prepared the fire for days. It's smoke and flames piled high into the air. The fire was burning hot. They threw the young boy in.

"O fire! Be cool and safe for Ibrahim!" It was an order from Allah. Ibrahim walked out safely. The fire did not harm him at all. It was a miracle, but there was much work to be done yet.

Rest Point

Even though he was still a young boy at the time, Ibrahim was so brave. Before we move onto the obstacles, lets do some word-work. Write each of the words below in sentences that show their meaning.

Ibrahim

smashed

idea

prepared

proud

blazing

rage

miracle

Jump the Fence

Now for the story events. Some of them are written below while others are missing. Fill in the empty spaces with the right events. Don't forget to number the circles in order!

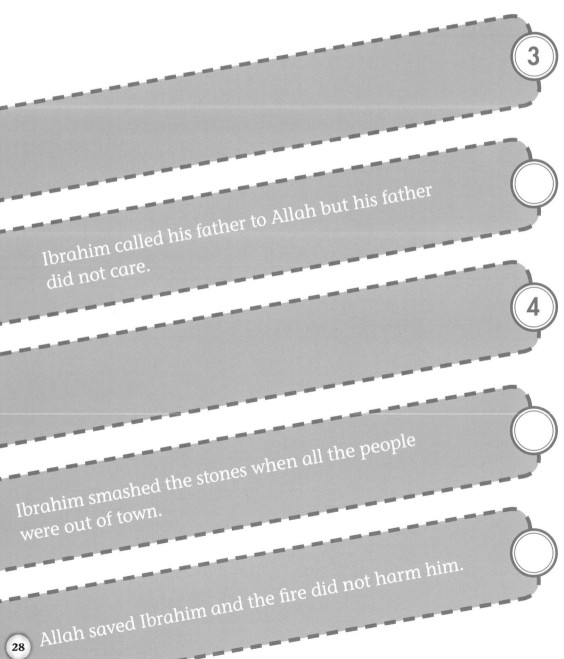

(3)

( )
Ibrahim called his father to Allah but his father did not care.

(4)

( )
Ibrahim smashed the stones when all the people were out of town.

( )
Allah saved Ibrahim and the fire did not harm him.

Cross the River

Write your answers to the following questions in the spaces provided. They follow on from the last obstacle. It couldn't be easier!

1. Describe how Ibrahim was as a young child?

....

2. What did Ibrahim tell his father?

....

3. What did Ibrahim's father say in reply?

....

4. What did Ibrahim do to the stones?

....

5. What did the people do with Ibrahim after he broke the stones?

....

Climb the Mountain

Complete the sentences in the statement by providing the reasons behind the events in the story.

Ibrahim waited until all the people were away

because ....

After breaking the stones, he left the axe on the

big stone so that .... The

people .... after seeing their

stones .... Ibrahim told them

the big stone did it so that ....

.... Ibrahim's plan was working because

....

The people still turned away because ....

.... They threw Ibrahim into a

fire, but ...., so it

did not harm Ibrahim.

the zam zam well

*It's time to start the second chapter in the story of Ibrahim. As before,
take a quick look at the words below to see which ones you already
know. We'll do some work on these and other words at the end.*

STRANGE

CURL

PEER

Ibrahim left his town. He traveled from place to place calling people to Islam. Ibrahim feared no one but Allah.

Ibrahim had a wife called Haajar. Their son Ismail was a Prophet of Islam. May Allah bless them all, *'Alay-himus-salaam.*

Ibrahim took his family far away to a desert valley. Ismail was still a baby then. There were no plants or signs of life around. It was a dry and empty land. Then Ibrahim did something rather strange...

He began to walk away leaving Haajar and Ismail behind. Haajar could not believe it.

"Why are you leaving us here?" she asked. Ibrahim kept on walking and did not reply. Haajar kept on asking.

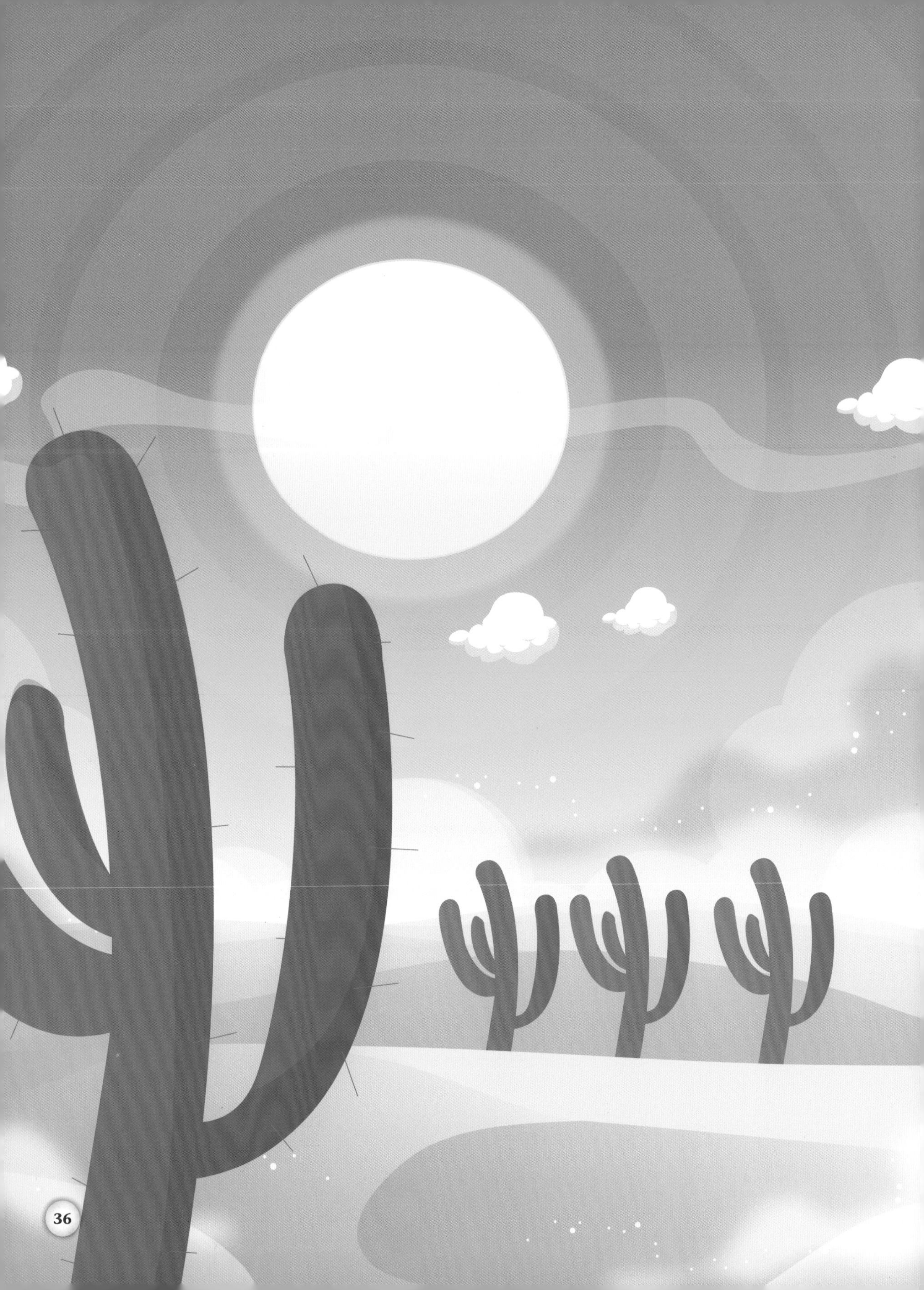

Clearly, the Prophet Ibrahim ﷺ would not leave his family alone in the hot desert without a good reason. What do you think his reason might be? Write your thoughts in the space below and then read on to see if you were right. The answer may be simpler than you think!

"Has Allah told you to leave us here?" she asked.

"Yes," said Ibrahim.

"Then He won't let us die like this." Haajar put her trust in Allah.

The desert heat was beating down hard. Haajar and Ismail were all alone and thirsty. Ismail cried, curling up into a ball. Haajar could not take it any longer. She got up and began looking for water.

She ran through the valley and up two hills, peering far and wide. There was no help in sight. Haajar looked down at her poor baby in the middle of the valley. Something strange was happening down there.

There was a spring gushing with water! Haajar came running down. It was a gift from Allah.

She scooped up the water and gave it to Ismail. Allah saved them with the miracle of the Zam Zam well.

Rest Point

Before you started this story, you were asked to make sure you understood the meanings of a few words. Now is the time to record your understanding. Write sentences using the words below.

travelled

Haajar

strange

curling

peering

gift

valley

Ismail

Jump the Fence

Below is a summary of the main events of the story. Fill each blank space using a suitable word from the list provided.

Ibrahim took his _____ to a plain land. He

left his family alone because _____ told him

to. Baby Ismail felt very _____. _____

went to look for water, but found no one. Allah made

_____ water spring from the ground.

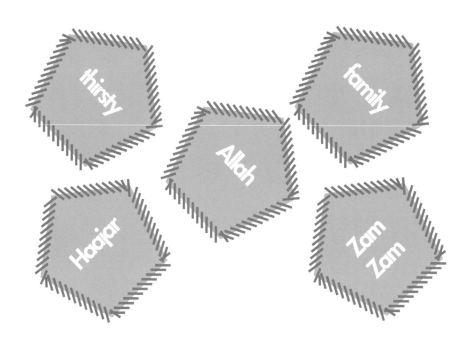

Cross the River

Now for a similar exercise, but looking in more detail at what happened. Think of a suitable word to fill each blank space in the statement below and then write it down in the spaces provided. There is no list of words to help you this time!

Ibrahim left his town and travelled to different places, calling people to .... His wife's name was ....and they had a son called ....Ismail was also a ....of Islam. Ibrahim took his wife and son to a...........................valley, and left them there as...........................had told him to do. When Haajar saw her baby son crying, she went to look for .... A spring of water ....near Ismail. Haajar ....to the water which is called............................

Climb the Mountain

There are just three questions in this mountain climb. Write your answers to the following questions in the spaces provided.

1. How can you tell that Haajar put her trust in Allah?

2. Which Islamic event does this story relate to and how?

3. What are the names of the two hills in the story?

Prepare for the next part of your journey by making sure you are familiar with the words mentioned below. We'll do some work on these and other words at the end of the story.

SACRIFICE

DEAR

SLICED

The desert valley grew into a town called Makkah. Ismail was a young boy now and Ibrahim came to visit him. That was when Ibrahim saw his dream.

"O my son! I saw in a dream that I was sacrificing you," said Ibrahim, "so tell me what you think." It was an order from Allah and it had to be done. But Ibrahim loved his son dearly.

How do you think Ismail will react to his father's question? Write your thoughts down in the space provided below and continue reading to see if you are correct.

....

....

....

....

....

....

....

....

....

....

....

"Do what Allah has ordered you to do," said Ismail. He never let Shaytaan get in the way. Ismail always did what Allah likes.

Ibrahim laid his son down. It was not an easy thing to do. He raised his knife and sliced it down.

It was all over. They passed the test and did what Allah said. Ismail was not harmed. Allah saved him and put a sheep in his place. It was all a big test.

Shaytaan's trick did not work with Ibrahim. He followed the truth and did what Allah likes. Allah took him as a close friend. Ibrahim won in the end.

Rest Point

How brave both father and son were! In the spaces provided, write each word in a suitable sentence that shows it's meanings.

SACRIFICE

DEARLY

SHEEP

MAKKAH

Jump the Fence

The story events are summarized in the sentences below, but they are all jumbled up!
Number them in the correct order using the squares on the ends.

Ismail told his father to do as Allah says.

Ismail was safe.

It was an order from Allah and it had to be done.

They both passed Allah's test.

Ibrahim saw a dream that he was sacrificing his son.

Ibrahim was about to sacrifice his son.

Ibrahim asked his son what he thought about it.

Allah put a sheep in place of Ismail.

Cross the River

Your drawing skills will be put to the test here. Write your answers to the following questions in the spaces provided. For the first question, help describe your answer by drawing a picture of the way Makkah used to look before compared to now.

1. How was Makkah different compared to before?

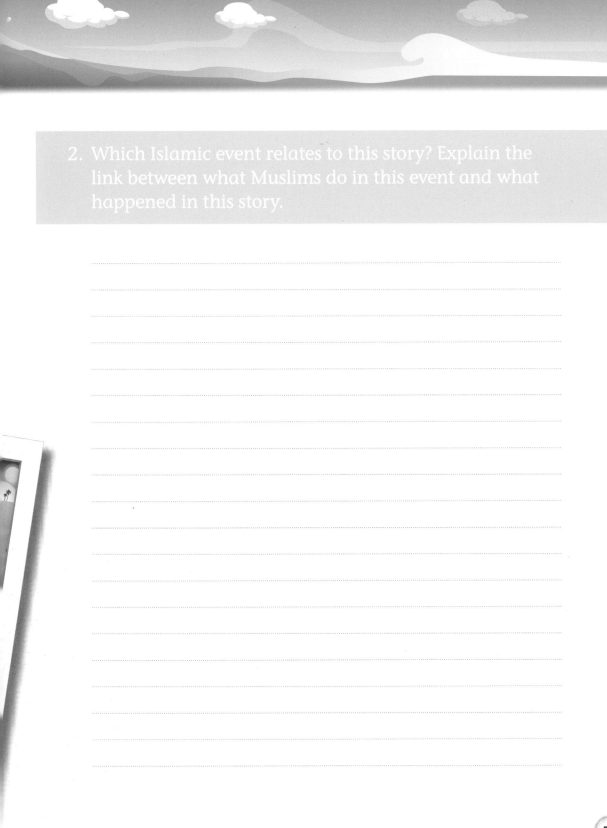

2. Which Islamic event relates to this story? Explain the link between what Muslims do in this event and what happened in this story.

Climb the Mountain

Climb this mountain by writing an appropriate question for each of the following answers in the spaces provided.

1. It was an order from Allah and had to be done.

....

....

2. Ismail did what Allah likes and told his father to do the same.

....

....

3. It was all a big test from Allah, and they both passed.

....

....

4. They followed the truth and did what Allah likes.

....

....

the first house

You have reached the last story in your journey. There is not much preparation to do here since the story is quite short. As always, take some time to ensure that you know what the words below mean. We'll do some work on these and other words at the end.

KA'BAH

HAJJ

Allah told Ibrahim to build the Ka'bah in Makkah. Ismail helped his father too. It was the first house made for people to pray to Allah alone.

Ibrahim called the people to visit the Ka'bah. Today millions of people answer Ibrahim's call. They come to Makkah to make Hajj. People come from every land, near and far. They come walking, riding, sailing and flying in on planes.

Rest Point

*There are only two words at this **Rest Point**, so we've made things a little different.*
Explain what you think Hajj is and draw a picture of the Ka'bah.

Hajj

Ka'bah

Jump the Fence

Write a summary below of the story you have just read. Write only one sentence in each triangle. There are no clues given here, so you may have to look back at the story for help.

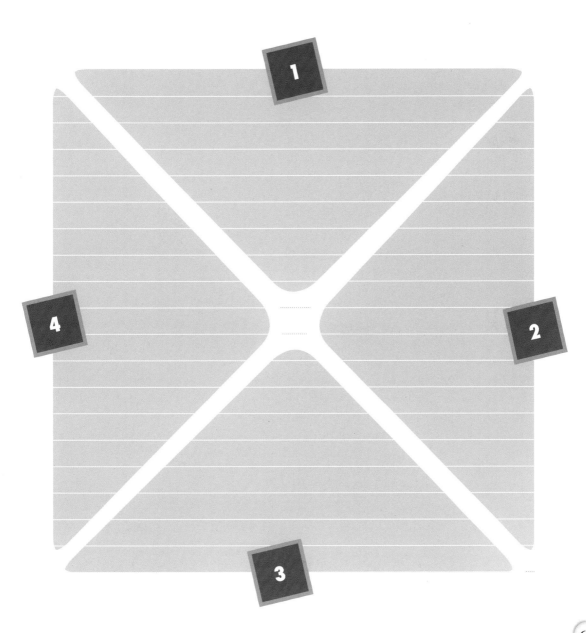

Cross the River

All of the statements below are incorrect. Cross this river by correcting each statement and rewriting them in the spaces provided.

Allah told Ibrahim to build the Ka'bah in Madinah.

1

Ibrahim helped Nuh build the Ka'bah.

3

2

Ibrahim called the birds to make Hajj.

The Ka'bah was the second house made for people to worship Allah alone.

4

Nuh built the Ka'bah.

5

Allah made the people answer the call of Ismail.

6

Climb the Mountain

Now for the final hurdle. Answer the questions below in the spaces provided.

1. Why is the Ka'bah special?

2. How can you tell people are answering the call of Ibrahim today?

the farewell mark

Every journey, no matter how long, must come to an end. You have come to the end of your journey through the life of Prophet Ibrahim ﷺ. One of the ways you can measure your success is through seeing how well you did in clearing the obstacles that came in your path. Suggested answers to each chapter are offered in the pages that follow. You are encouraged to have your progress marked.

However, there is more to measuring your success than just clearing the obstacles. One of the most valuable measures is your own thoughts on what you have learnt and enjoyed most. Hopefully, you will take away a treasure chest of lessons from this wonderful and important story, and continue learning more about it in the future. This chapter offers you the chance to judge for yourself what was your most valuable farewell mark.

At the end of a journey, it's always nice to pause and think over what you can most benefit from. Think hard about what were the most valuable lessons you learnt during this journey. Take a moment to think again and select one lesson, idea or thought that you will take away from your experience...

Did you really think
it was all over?

Shaytaan was still out there making his call. He played his trick on a king called Fir'own. He thought he was god and never prayed to Allah. Fir'own had a powerful army and used it to harm his people. Something had to be done to stop him...

Discover what happens in the story of Musa ﷺ.

a clever thought

Section	Answer	Comments
	He would accuse the biggest idol of breaking the other ones so that his people would understand the reality of what they were doing.	
	Ibrahim: Ibrahim was a Prophet of Allah. **Smashed:** Ibrahim smashed the idols into small pieces. **Idea:** Ibrahim had a clever idea in mind. **Prepared:** The traveller was well prepared for his journey. **Proud:** The people were too proud to admit the truth. **Blazing:** The blazing fire burnt the house down. **Rage:** People were shouting in anger and rage. **Miracle:** Ibrahim was saved from the fire by a miracle from Allah.	*The answers offered here are by way of suggestion only. Credit should be given for any valid response.*
	1. Ibrahim called his father to Allah but his father did not listen. **2.** Ibrahim smashed the stones when all the people were out of town. **3.** The people were angry, but Ibrahim taught them a clever lesson. **4.** The people tried to burn Ibrahim. **5.** Allah saved Ibrahim and the fire did not harm him.	
	1. Brave. **2.** 'Why do you pray to stones? They cannot harm you or bring you any good.' **3.** 'If you do not stop, I will stone you!' **4.** Ibrahim broke the idols. **5.** Ibrahim's people tried to burn him in a big fire.	
	Ibrahim waited until all the people were away because **he had an idea in mind**. After breaking the stones, he left the axe on the big stone so that **he could say that it broke the others**. The people **were very angry** after seeing their stones **broken into little bits**. Ibrahim told them the big stone did it so that **it would force them to think about why they pray to them**. Ibrahim's plan was working because **the people realized that the stones cannot talk**. The people still turned away because **they were too proud**. They threw Ibrahim into a fire, but **Allah ordered it to be cool,** so it did not harm him..	

the zam zam well

Section	Answer	Comments
	Allah told him to do so.	
	Travelled: Ibrahim travelled to different lands. **Haajar:** Haajar was the wife of Ibrahim. **Strange:** Haajar saw something strange happening in the valley. **Curling:** The baby was curling up into a ball out of thirst. **Peering:** Haajar was peering far and wide from the top of the hill. **Gift:** Zam Zam water is a blessing and gift from Allah. **Valley:** A valley is the area between the two hills. **Ismail:** Ismail was the son of Ibrahim.	*The answers offered here are by way of suggestion only. Credit should be given for any valid response.*
	family • Allah • thirsty • Haajar • Zam Zam	
	Allah • Haajar • Ismail • Prophet • desert • Allah • water • gushed • ran • Zam Zam •	
	1. Her words; 'Allah will not let us die like this,' show that she had trust in Allah. **2.** Sa'ee during Hajj and 'Umrah. The actions of Sa'ee trace the running of Haajar between the hills. **3.** Safa and Marwa.	*The answers offered here are brief. Elaboration may be explored by the respondent. These questions also require independent research.*

the big test

Section	Answer	Comments
	Ismail was brave and told his father to do as Allah says.	
	Sacrifice: Ibrahim was ordered to sacrifice his son. **Dearly:** Ibrahim loved his son dearly. **Sheep:** The sheep was found near the farm fence. **Makkah:** Zam Zam water is found in Makkah.	*The answers offered here are by way of suggestion only. Credit should be given for any valid response.*
	1. Ibrahim saw a dream in which he was sacrificing his son. **2.** It was an order from Allah and it had to be done. **3.** Ibrahim asked his son what he thought about it. **4.** Ismail told his father to do as Allah says. **5.** Ibrahim was about to sacrifice his son. **6.** Allah put a sheep in place of Ismail. **7.** Ismail was safe. **8.** They both passed Allah's test.	
	1. Makkah was now a town compared to being a plain desert before. (Picture to show empty desert valley). **2.** Eid Al-Adha, and the sacrifice Muslims make on this day.	
	1. Why did Ibrahim have to do what he saw in his dream? **2.** Why did Ismail tell his father to do what Allah says? **3.** Why was sacrificing Ismail not an easy thing to do for Ibrahim? **4.** Why did Ismail not have to be sacrificed?	

the first house

Section	Answer	Comments
	Hajj: Hajj is the pilgrimage to the Ka'bah and one of the five pillars of Islam. **Ka'bah:** A picture of the Ka'bah.	*The answers offered here are by way of suggestion only. Credit should be given for any valid response.*
	1. Allah told Ibrahim to build the Ka'bah. **2.** Allah told Ibrahim to call the people for Hajj even though there was no one around. **3.** Allah made people answer the call. **4.** Today, people from all over the world come for Hajj.	
	1. Allah told Ibrahim to build the Ka'bah in Makkah. **2.** Ismail helped Ibrahim build the Ka'bah. **3.** Ibrahim called the people to make Hajj. **4.** The Ka'bah was the first house made for people to worship Allah alone. **5.** Ibrahim built the Ka'bah. **6.** Allah made the people answer the call of Ibrahim.	
	1. Allah chose it as the first house to be made for the worship of Allah. **2.** Millions of people around the world come to perform Hajj.